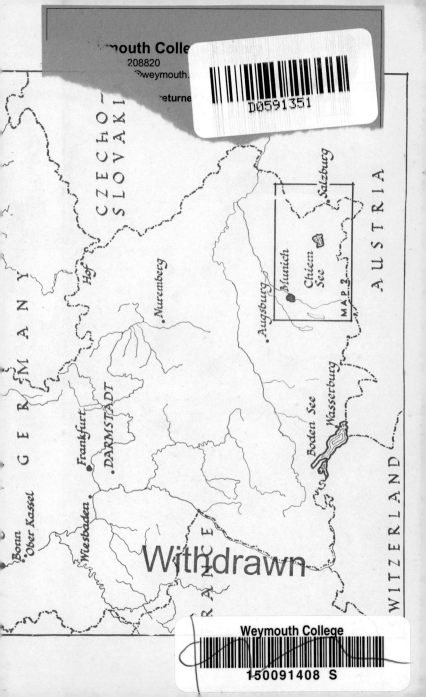

# The History of
# The Concrete Roofing Tile

1 *A Diamond-Pattern Concrete Tile, c. 1848, made by Adolph Kroher, the inventor of the tile*

*The History of*

# The Concrete Roofing Tile

*Its Origin and Development
in Germany*

by

CHARLES DOBSON

*With Technical Notes by*
F. L. BRADY M.Sc. A.R.I.C.

London
B. T. BATSFORD LTD

© Marley Tile Company Limited

*First Published* 1959

MADE AND PRINTED IN GREAT BRITAIN BY
TONBRIDGE PRINTERS LTD. TONBRIDGE
FOR THE PUBLISHERS
B. T. BATSFORD LTD.
4 FITZHARDINGE ST. PORTMAN SQUARE LONDON W.I

# Foreword

In this foreword I would like to say how much I feel industry will be indebted to Mr. Dobson for the work that has been done in writing this book.

A few words as to the origin of the book may not come amiss. My interest in concrete roofing tiles is no secret. Their history in this country goes back about sixty years, but it was generally known that they had been made on the Continent for a longer period. Just where, how and when and by whom was not known. It seemed worth while finding out. During numerous visits to the Continent during the past thirty years I had been led to think that South Germany would be worth exploring from this point of view. The opportunity arose for my lifelong friend Mr. Dobson to undertake an investigation and he has, I believe, answered all these questions, at the same time giving us a picture of the personalities concerned in the growth of the concrete roofing tile. The personal facts of any industry are always more easily understood and generally appreciated than the bare technical facts. We see the why and wherefore of it all.

Let us hope that Mr. Dobson will continue his research in this and other countries and give future generations the record of an industry which I am sure will continue to grow here and elsewhere, as it has done particularly during the last forty years.

OWEN A. AISHER
*Chairman of the Marley Tile Company Limited*

v

# Preface

THE assembly of the information given in these pages has been made possible through the willing help given to me by many people in England, Germany, Austria and Denmark. Only a few of them are named in the text, but to all of them I offer my thanks.

To the Directors of the Marley Tile Company Limited I shall always be grateful for the chance they have given me to study pitched roofing materials and methods in Germany, and in the parts of Austria and Denmark which adjoin that country. For more than thirty years, until my retirement, the pitched roof, with its coverings of slates, clay and concrete tiles, thatch and shingles had been both my business and my hobby, and these visits on behalf of the Marley Tile Company have therefore been enjoyable and instructive.

Mr. F. L. Brady, M.Sc., A.R.I.C., the Technical Director of the Company, has admirably supplemented the narrative by his notes on some of the tiles that I brought back.

Herr Ernst Uhde, the Director of the *Marley Werke GMBH* at Luthe-Wunstorf near Hanover, has given me much valuable help, as also have his managers and staff at Düsseldorf, Frankfurt, Munich, Hamburg, Lübeck and Kiel.

Mr. R. W. Parks, the Secretary of the British Cast Concrete Federation, gave me a good start by arranging for me to meet, at Bonn, Dr. A. Nauen, the General Manager of the *Bundesverband der Betonsteinindustrie*, the German counterpart of the British Cast Concrete Federation. Mr. Parks also gave me an introduction to Herr H. Peters, a well-known concrete engineer at Wiesbaden.

Mr. R. H. Baumgarten, who was the doyen of the concrete roofing tile industry in England, and who has, to our great regret, died recently, gave me much assistance in the preliminary stages.

The maps have been drawn for us by Mr. Roger G. Simmons, A.R.I.B.A., who was a fighter pilot during the War, and was shot down over North Africa. As a prisoner of war in Stalag Luft III, the camp from which the 'Wooden Horse' party made their escape, he was a member of the small team that prepared the documents, including the maps, for the escape party. It is therefore altogether fitting that Mr. Simmons should have done our maps.

Finally, I want to add a tribute to my wife, and to my secretary, Miss Jeanne Barker. My wife has relieved me of all the mundane troubles that are inseparable from such itineraries as are involved in the kind of work that I have been doing, and has seen to it that our daily journeys have not degenerated into stampedes. Miss Barker came with us on two of our journeys, made verbatim notes of our meetings at a score of places, and took many of the photographs.

# Contents

# List of Illustrations

## THE MAPS

xi

# The History of
# The Concrete Roofing Tile

*Its Origin and Development in Germany*

THIS book has been compiled with the single aim of interesting those who may like to learn something more about the origin and development of the concrete roofing tile than is generally known in England. It is neither a textbook on concrete tiling nor an essay extolling the tile.

The narrative is an abridged version of the mass of information that I have gathered in Germany, Austria and Denmark, most of it during the five visits that I have made since August 1957 at the invitation of the Marley Tile Company. Most of the photographs were taken during those visits, but a few were taken on earlier occasions.

I have tried to ensure that the dates given for the manufacture of tiles are accurate within a year or two. Where such a degree of accuracy has not been possible I have given the period during which the tiles were almost certainly made.

This book adds only a little to what is already known in Germany about the history of the concrete tile, but it can perhaps claim to have added a touch of human interest that would have been inappropriate in the more technical books that have been published here and in Germany.

Several authors have written about German pitched roofing with much greater authority than I could pretend to. I have read a good deal of the work of E. Probst and A. Althammer in translation, and have, on two occasions, had the pleasure and privilege of spending a few hours with Herr Althammer in Munich, discussing with him the German concrete tile, and looking through the unrivalled

*Fig. 2*

*Adolph Kroher (1825–1892) from an oil painting done in 1867 by August Heyn. The signature is from a letter written by Kroher in 1890*

collection of photographs of concrete tiled roofs that he has taken in most parts of Germany. Herr Althammer is the author of *Die Betondachsteine*, the standard German book on concrete roof tiling; he wrote it in 1954 for the Bundes-verband der Betonsteinindustrie—the German counterpart of our British Cast Concrete Federation.

There must be many people in England who think, as I once thought, that the concrete tile was invented here, and that it was first made soon after the 1914–18 War, at a time when the supply of slates and clay tiles was inadequate to meet the demand. The facts are quite different: the first concrete tiles were made in the eighteen-forties at Staudach, a tiny agricultural village in Southern Bavaria, only a few miles north of the Austrian frontier. And the tile was invented and pioneered by a young man named Adolph Kroher, who was at the time in no way connected with the building industry. I have visited the Kroher house at Staudach five times and have learned from Adolph Kroher's grandson and great-granddaughter a good part of what has become for me 'The Staudach Story'.

Staudach is in the extreme south of Germany. At Wedel, in Schleswig-Holstein, towards the northern boundary of the country, I have twice met Herr Heinrich Jörgensen, the seventy-five-year-old son of J. P. Jörgensen, a Danish mason who played a great part in the introduction of concrete products, including concrete tiles, into North Germany.

## The Staudach Story

One morning in the late autumn of 1957 I heard the story of young Kroher's first visit to Staudach and of his later career; and I heard it in what was surely the most appropriate setting—the farmhouse which he bought when he introduced the concrete tile to the German and Austrian building industries.

*Fig. 3*

*Staudach: the Kroher farmhouse, roofed with diamond-pattern tiles made by Adolph Kroher*

I count this as one of the more memorable experiences of my life. We sat in the living-room of the farmhouse, a room cosily furnished in what we should call a Victorian fashion, its most prominent features a big square glaze-tiled Bavarian stove, a grandfather clock, and an ornate sideboard with cupboards underneath, containing the old correspondence of the Staudacher-Cementfabrik, the company which Kroher founded in 1858. I have some of that correspondence with me as I write. The letters are written in a fine old German copperplate hand—one of them signed by Adolph Kroher himself, another by his son.

A friend of many years' standing, Robert von Benda of Lübeck, had come down to interpret for me, and while he and Fraulein Erika Kroher talked on in German of her great-grandfather, I sat looking out of the window seeing the pale November sun shining on the first snow on the Bavarian Alps. We had come out from Munich that morning in a Marley Volkswagen along the autobahn that runs from Munich to Salzburg and the roadmen were already setting up the hurdles beside the road as barriers against the drifting snow that was shortly to come.

Here is the Staudach story as I have put it together from what was learned during my visits to the village, from conversations and correspondence with Herr Eugen Kroher —Adolph's grandson—and from official documents.

Adolph Kroher was born at Hof, in Bavaria, on the 3rd May, 1825: I can be quite precise as to family dates because I have a copy of the family tree which Fraulein Erika Kroher prepared during the war. Here are the entries that are relevant to the narrative.

| | |
|---|---|
| Adolph Kroher | 3 May 1825—23 April 1892 |
| Adolph Kroher | 11 July 1855—30 January 1934 |
| Eugen Kroher | 19 July 1882— |
| Erika Kroher | |

One summer in the eighteen-forties, in a year that cannot be precisely determined, young Kroher spent his holiday at a guest house in Grassau, a village only a few kilometres from Staudach: he could hardly have conjectured that this visit to Grassau was to prove the most important milestone in his life.

At Grassau he made the acquaintance of a forester named Pauli, and of a man named Graf, the manager of the local salt works. These two men were, he found, supplementing their regular incomes by making a stucco from a local mineral deposit, which they burned in a primitive fashion and mixed with the sharp sand from the Tiroler Ache—the river from which Staudach gets its name. Much

*Fig. 4*

*Staudach: the natural cement quarry in 1901. The buildings are roofed with Kroher's diamond-pattern tiles*

6

of the rendering which Pauli and Graf used on houses in Staudach and neighbouring villages is said to be still in good condition.

Kroher became interested in this activity of Pauli and Graf—so interested that he decided to see if there was a possibility of using this mineral deposit, which proved to be a quick-setting natural cement, for the purposes for which Portland cement was later used.

Adolph Kroher sent samples of the deposit to Vienna for testing, the results were satisfactory, and he set about trying to establish the manufacture of the cement on a commercial scale. Pauli and Graf were, when Kroher came on the scene, making it only 'by the bushel', as his grandson has told me. It needed a man of vision, initiative and business acumen to found the industry, and Adolph Kroher proved to be that man.

In the family tree he is described as 'Kaufmann und Fabrikant'—merchant and manufacturer—and for a number of years he played this dual role. He was a manufacturer of Staudach cement and of concrete products, but his regular income came from his occupation as a paper merchant. He bought wholesale from a firm of paper makers in Augsburg, and sold to retail shops within accessible distances from Augsburg.

Herr Eugen Kroher has shown me the handsome cloth-bound brochure which his father issued early in this century. It bears on its cover the inscription:

STAUDACHER CEMENTFABRIK

ADOLPH KROHER

IN

STAUDACH

WIEN 1873        NUREMBURG 1882

ANERKENNUNG DIPLOM    GROSSE BRONZENE MEDAILLE

Handelsgerichtlichte–Eintragung

1858

This inscription is of importance in the story, particularly the reference to the Diploma of Merit awarded to Kroher at the International Exhibition in Vienna in 1873. The wording before the date 1858 records that the business was registered in that year with the Chamber of Commerce: it had, of course, been a going concern for some years before 1858.

He had to overcome at least one major difficulty before he could start his cement works. At that time timber was among the most valuable of Bavaria's assets, and a source of considerable revenue to the kingdom. Now the site of the intended quarry belonged to the State Forest Administration and was well-wooded. The Administration was reluctant to give it over to one who would destroy the timber and put the land to what must have seemed to them a vandalistic use. Kroher was determined to acquire the site and, although still a young man, he had a good head for business. He put to the Administration a proposition to which it finally agreed. Kroher bought the farm which his grandson now occupies, and which at that time had a right to take 29.5 cubic metres of firewood per annum, a right which was valued at 800 gold marks. Under the arrangement which he made with the Forest Administration, he relinquished the right to take the firewood, and in return the Administration sold to Kroher the land containing the natural cement.

An added advantage was that Kroher, by occupying the farm, became a burgher of Staudach, a matter of some importance to one who hoped to establish himself as a business man in the district.

So far the concrete tile has not come into our Staudach story, and you may well ask how we know that the first tiles were made there, and what part Adolph Kroher played in the invention and development of the tile. Here are the answers to both questions.

8

In 1907 the German Association of Manufacturers of Concrete Products set up a committee to report on what had been learned about the behaviour of the concrete tile in Germany. The committee met at Guben, a small town about eighty miles south-west of Berlin, and at that time one of the centres of concrete tile production in Germany. Herr Althammer gives 1883 as the date when production started in Guben.

The opening paragraph of the Guben Committee's Report says that 'the views regarding the year in which the concrete roofing tile was first made have been, until recently, widely divergent, but it is clear that the diamond-pattern tile is appreciably older than the interlocking tile. The first roofing tiles to be made of cement were prepared in 1844 in the Kroher Cement Factory at Staudach in Bavaria . . . These tiles were exhibited at the Arnhem Exhibition in 1879: according to official attestations these had been on roofs for thirty-five years without showing any sign of weathering or porosity. Because of their age they were stronger than the newly-made tiles which were shown at the Exhibition.'

Similar information is given in a 1927 article—'The Cement Roofing Tile'—published in Charlottenburg. Herr Althammer gives Staudach pride of place, and other authorities agree.

As to the part played by Adolph Kroher, my conversations at Staudach have convinced me that he was indeed the first man in Germany and, so far as we know, in the world, to make a concrete roofing tile. In May 1919 Eugen Kroher wrote an article for the German 'Clay Industry Journal' in which he said that 'the manufacture of these tiles was started in Staudach, a small mountain village in the Chiemgau, where cement tiles were first made in the forties of last century from the quick-setting local Staudacher cement, as a house industry for workers who were unemployed during the winter'. It was his grandfather, Eugen Kroher assures

9

me, who started this home industry, and it was his grandfather who first recognised the value of the quick-setting properties of the cement. The tile could be made only with a cement that would allow the removal of the tile from its mould within a few hours of its being made. Portland cement, which is now used almost universally for the manufacture of concrete tiles, had been invented in England in 1824, but was unknown anywhere in Germany until 1856.

Eugen Kroher's statements are supported by external evidence. During my travels in Germany, Austria and Denmark I have visited most, if not all, of the areas in which concrete tiles have been made, and nowhere have I found tiles so old as those to be seen in and around Staudach. It was Adolph Kroher and none other who invented the concrete tile, and who founded an industry that is now world-wide in its range.

Kroher was a builder and farmer as well as a manufacturer of cement and of concrete products, and his three activities dovetailed together most satisfactorily. That he had a substantial business is shown by the fact that at one time, after the Vienna Exhibition in 1873, he was employing as many as one hundred and twenty men, sixty of them Italians whom he had recruited by making a special journey to Italy for the purpose. All of these Italians were young men, and many of them were skilled and versatile artisans. Many of the buildings still existing in Staudach and Grassau were the work of Kroher's young Italians.

Kroher switched his men from the factories to the farm, or to building, according to the weather and the demand for his products. In very bad weather all his men worked in the factories; in good weather the elderly Germans would be on the land, while the Italians were doing building and decorating.

The Diploma of Merit which Adolph Kroher received at

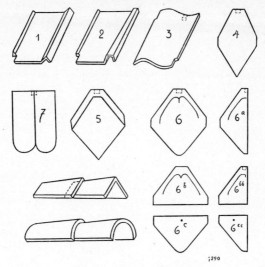

*Bild 7    Zementdachsteine*

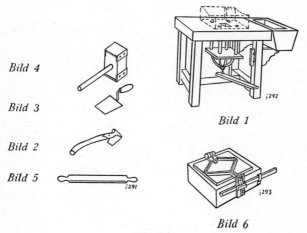

*Fig. 5*

*Illustrations from Eugen Kroher's article in the May 1919
German 'Clay Industry Journal'*

*Fig. 6*

*Eugen Kroher and his wife at the entrance to the farmstead*

*Fig. 7*

*Eugen Kroher demonstrating the device used by his grandfather for the manufacture of diamond-pattern, or slate shaped, concrete tiles. Output about 125 tiles per day*

Vienna was awarded for his diamond-pattern tiles, and as a direct result the Austrian Government gave him the largest order that he ever had, an order that would be considered large even today. It was for all the tiles needed for the roofs of the stations, signal boxes, workmen's houses, and other ancillary buildings of the Tauern Railway, then being built southwards from Salzburg. The tiles were packed in hay and carried in horse wagons or on pack-horses into Austria. Fraulein Erika Kroher told me of her pride in finding, when she travelled on the railway in 1945, that most of the roofs still displayed her great-grandfather's tiles. On a recent

Fig. 8                              Fig. 9

*Two views of the device invented by Adolph Kroher for making his
early diamond-pattern concrete tiles, as described by his grandson
on page 20.*

*The base plate, here seen in position, is of wood, and the paper on
it is the 'release agent' which prevented the adhesion of the tile to the
base plate. Adolph Kroher used jute sacking in preference to paper
as a release agent, and the pattern of the sacking is still clearly
discernible on the back of tiles that he made as long ago as 1870.*

*In these photographs the steel ring is closed ready for the reception
of the concrete*

journey down the Tauern Railway, I noticed that most of
these roofs are now covered with asbestos-cement.

In his article, Eugen Kroher mentions the different shapes
of tile with which his father had experimented, and the
illustration which we reproduce shows these types. It was
No. 6, the diamond pattern, which Kroher finally decided

was the best shape for concrete, and it is a venerable No. 6 which is the subject of our frontispiece. He abandoned altogether the making of some of the types, but he continued to manufacture his pantile, No. 3, of which we have an example made in about 1870. We also have one of the

*Fig. 10*

*A wooden 'forme' used by Adolph Kroher for making concrete pantiles. Output about 180 tiles per day*

wooden moulds on which these pantiles were made before the iron pallet came into use. In Bavaria this concrete pantile is called the *Belgische Ziegel*, or Belgian tile.

Kroher favoured the diamond pattern for several reasons. It was easily carried up the roof, and was easily laid by semi-skilled men; it was less fragile than any of the types

14

made with rolls or other features; it was easily packed and
transported by horse wagon; the rainfall is very heavy in
the Salzburg area, and Adolph Kroher found that the
tendency of moisture to travel along the joints between
adjacent tiles was less in the case of the diamond pattern

*Fig. 11*

*A modern machine producing 'Anglia' concrete pantiles. Output
about 60 tiles per minute*

than any other kind; it was easy to walk up a roof covered
with these tiles—an important matter because in Germany,
as in Scotland, the chimneys are swept from the top
downwards.

For these reasons Kroher encouraged the use of his
diamond-pattern tile, and in doing so he was following a

15

*Fig. 12*

*A Roman stone slate from a Roman villa near Woodstock in Oxfordshire. The nail is the original iron nail that was in the slate when it was unearthed. This slate is now in the Langley Museum at 163 Borough High Street, London*

traditional usage that goes back at least to the Romans. The photograph of a Roman stone slate from the Cotswolds shows the similarity between it and the German diamond-pattern tile. When laid on the roof the resemblance is even more striking.

Going ahead a few years—when the Austrian Hatchek invented asbestos-cement roofing his first tile was almost exactly similar in size and shape to Kroher's tile.

The older German builders had what might be thought an exaggerated regard for the shapes of their slates and tiles: they took into account the undoubted fact that water running down a roof tends to follow the line of the lower edge of the slate or flat tile, if it slopes instead of being horizontal, and will discharge at the lowest point on to the unit in the course below. This explains their penchant for the diamond-pattern tile, and for their unusual method of fixing slates on roofs such as those seen in the Goslar photographs.

The matter is too involved for full discussion here, but I would mention that this same tendency of water to follow the line of the tail of a tile partly accounts for the effectiveness of the English laced valley in plain tiling.

The Kroher family ceased to make concrete products in 1929, and the cement works passed into other hands. Eugen Kroher told me that the chief cause was the inflation of the German currency, but he added that the manufacture of tiles had already become unprofitable because of the formidable competition of the clay tile. The clay machine-made single-lap tile had been invented in 1840 by the brothers Joseph and Xavier Gilardoni in Alsace. They took out a patent in England for a similar tile on the 27th April, 1855: this is generally regarded as the first English patent for a true interlocking tile. The Gilardoni family still make single-lap roofing tiles.

Quite early in his career Adolph Kroher had started a

*Fig. 13*

*Goslar, Hartz Mountains. This illustration and fig. 14 show the attractive ways in which the German slater uses his material on roofs and walls. The valley in this photograph is formed in slate, and is called a Herzkehlen, or heart valley*

*Fig. 14*

*Goslar, Hartz Mountains (see fig. 13)*

'Do it Yourself' scheme for potential users of his cement. It was the difficulty of transporting tiles over long distances that caused him to do this. He sold his cement to anybody who wanted to make tiles, and with it the moulds or presses, and printed instructions for making the tiles. His scheme resulted in a more widespread use of Staudach cement and Kroher tiles, but it had the long-term disadvantage that the manufacture of tiles was done by amateurs who did not understand the importance of a correct mixing of the cement and aggregate.

I am fairly certain that the 1866 Neukirchen tile (Figs. 39 and 40) which Mr. Brady mentions in his notes, and which consists almost entirely of Staudach cement in particles up to $\frac{1}{4}$ in., was made by an amateur. My own view is that Kroher's 'Do it Yourself' scheme, excellent as it must have seemed at its inception, did a disservice to the cause that Kroher himself had at heart—the development of the concrete roofing tile. Eugen Kroher told me that many Tyrolese peasants still make tiles on his grandfather's machines.

One of those machines is No. 6 in the illustrations to Eugen Kroher's article. On my last visit to Staudach he came with me to Piesenhausen, a few kilometres away, where Herr Mathias Gassner, the owner of a concrete products works, still uses the apparatus. This particular piece of apparatus was made by the original Adolph Kroher, and it has therefore been in continuous use for about eighty years: he died in 1892. Eugen Kroher gave me a demonstration of its use, and it was then that I took the photographs on page 12. In his article he describes the operation of the apparatus thus:

'On a square wooden block, a steel ring corresponding to the mould, which could be opened like tongs, was so fitted that it could first be opened about a hinge to allow the base plate to be inserted, and secondly held closed by a special clamping device fixed to the side opposite to the hinge and then pressed down on to the base plate. After the mortar had been pounded, scraped off and smoothed, both legs of the ring were unclamped, pulled apart sideways, and folded over backwards so that the base plate with the tile was free . . . In this way a worker could produce, on an average, 125 slate shaped tiles per day.'

Eugen Kroher uses the term 'slate shaped tiles'—further evidence, perhaps, that his grandfather based the design of the tile on the old German kind of slate roofing.

That is the Staudach story, but before we turn our attention to other parts of Germany we may usefully remind ourselves of the kind of roofing world into which the concrete tile was born. Four kinds of pitched roof coverings were then in use in Germany: shingles, thatch, clay tiles and slate, and each type is illustrated here. In those days of poor roads and very limited transport facilities, all ordinary building was necessarily done with local materials.

In the forest areas of Germany, the wood shingle was the ordinary roofing material. The Staudach farmhouse had cleft shingles when Kroher bought it: the sawn shingle was a later innovation. He stripped off the shingles, raised the pitch of the rafters by a few degrees, and covered the roof with his own tiles, the ones you see in the photograph.

Rattau is only a few kilometres from Staudach: the photograph is interesting for two or three reasons. The low-pitched roof, originally of cleft shingles, is now covered with clay machine-made single-lap tiles. They are held down near the verge by lengths of timber and stones—a method familiar to all visitors to Germany, Austria and Switzerland. The firewood is stacked with meticulous care under the shelf on which stand the thin fir branches that are destined to form the tripod supports of the small hayricks that are usual in districts which have a heavy rainfall. These small

21

*Fig. 15*

*Rattau, near Staudach: clay interlocking tiles, held down at the verge
by timber and stones. Cleft shingles on end wall*

*Fig. 16*

*Krusendorf, near Kiel: old German reed thatching, moss-covered*

23

tripods are called *heuhütten*—hay huts. The walls are still clad with cleft shingles.

In Schleswig-Holstein, an agricultural region, most of the roofs were of reed thatch, and reeds are still cultivated in the marshlands along the Elbe below Hamburg, as one of the Haseldorf photographs shows. The thatch seen in the Krusendorf picture is covered with moss, to such an extent indeed that the thatch itself is hardly visible. Reeds are an extremely durable material, and I am told that a life of eighty years is not unusual. Krusendorf is on the very bad, but very pretty coast road from Kiel to Eckernförde.

As illustrations of old German clay tiling I have chosen a photograph of beaver-tailed tiles on a roof at Wasserburg-am-Bodensee, on the German side of Lake Constance, and another taken at Rothenburg-ob-der-Tauber. The southern part of Germany abounds with examples of this beaver-tailed tiling. The rounded lower edge of the tile gives a pleasing appearance to the roof, and it conforms to the old German ideas on tile shape to which I have already referred. Adolph Kroher experimented with this type in concrete but abandoned it because of its weight when laid to a double lap, like our slates and plain tiles. The Wasserburg beaver-tails are laid to a single lap, with thin fir strips about $1\frac{1}{2}$ in. wide under the vertical joints—a seemingly ineffective way of keeping out the wet, but it works fairly well. At Quick-born, Herr Paul Rademacher showed me a shed in his garden, the walls and roofs covered with a rather similar tile in concrete: here the vertical joints between adjacent tiles have zinc strips underneath, about 1 in. wide, plus a welt along each edge. This type of tile, Herr Rademacher said, was never very successful, and its use had long ago been abandoned.

The last in the list of old German kinds of roofing is German slating. Anybody who has been to Goslar in the Hartz Mountains will agree that here is to be seen the old

*Fig. 17*

*Wasserburg-am-Bodensee, Lake Constance: beaver-tailed clay tiling at the Strand Hotel St. Georg*

*Fig. 18*

*Rothenburg-ob-der-Tauber: 'a perfectly preserved medieval city wall, with ramparts, gates and turrets,' says Nagel. Here is one of the turrets, and part of the wall, both roofed with clay beaver-tailed tiles*

26

*Fig. 19*

*Haseldorf, near Hamburg: The Oppenschilden Mausoleum built by J. P. Jörgensen in c. 1871*

27

German *schieferdach* in profusion and at its best: much of the craftsmanship is superb. The two photographs show the method of application on roof and walls.

The roofs seen in this set of photographs typify the kinds of roofing common in Germany at the time when Adolph Kroher introduced his new material to the builders of Bavaria and Austria.

## The Haseldorf Story

Chance had played a part in Adolph Kroher's debut into the concrete roofing tile industry, and it was responsible for bringing J. P. Jörgensen to the Holstein village of Haseldorf. It came about in this way.

Until 1864 Schleswig-Holstein was occupied by the Danes, and it was not until the end of the 1864 War between Germany and Denmark that the frontier was pushed north to Flensburg. The Danish Town Major of Haseldorf before the war was Kammerherr Oppenschilden, and he found himself so comfortably settled in Haseldorf that he decided to spend the rest of his life there. What is of greater significance to us, he decided to have a mausoleum built in the grounds of his estate, so that even after death he would, so to speak, be at Haseldorf.

Wishing to have the mausoleum built by a Dane, and perhaps finding that skilled labour was not available in the agricultural region of Holstein, he sent to Copenhagen for a first-class man. Jörgen Peter Jörgensen was chosen and he came down to Haseldorf in 1871. He had been born in 1852 at Faaborg on the Danish island of Fühnen in the Baltic, so he was only nineteen years old when he came to Germany. He was, it may be thought, rather young to take the responsibility for building the mausoleum that you see in the photograph, but a fairly detailed knowledge of all that Jörgensen achieved in later life makes one feel sure that

28

*Fig. 20*

*Jörgen Peter Jörgensen—a photograph taken at one of his factories, c. 1903. The workman is taking concrete bricks from a machine patented by Jörgensen* even at nineteen or twenty years of age he would have been quite capable of doing the work.

There is not, so far as I know, any natural building stone in Holstein, and it may be that because Jörgensen was already skilled in the manufacture of artificial stone he was chosen for this onerous task. The walls of the mausoleum are of concrete, its Ionic columns are of what Jörgensen called *Danisch marmor*—Danish marble. You may think it an eccentric trait in Oppenschilden's character, perhaps even a macabre one, to have his mausoleum built in his lifetime, and within view of his house, but I understand that it would not have been thought odd at that time.

I have closely examined the building, and except for a little decay here and there the materials are apparently as good as when Jörgensen made them; and the ceiling under the dome is as fine a piece of craftsmanship of its kind as I have seen anywhere. The estate is now owned by the Durchlaucht Schönaich-Carolath, who readily gave me permission to inspect and photograph the mausoleum.

Young Jörgensen found, like his employer Oppenschilden, that he liked Haseldorf and its people so well that he did not want to go back to Denmark. In fact, he fell in love with a German girl whom he met at a dance, married her and settled down, first at Haseldorf and later at the nearby town of Wedel.

Most of this story of Jörgensen's life has been learned from his son, a retired engineer now seventy-five years old, living in the Schulestrasse at Wedel, within a stone's throw of the site of the factory shown in the 1901 photograph.

Did Jörgensen introduce the concrete roofing tile into North Germany? We do not know, but he did so much for the concrete products industry in Schleswig-Holstein that it would not surprise me to learn that he was the first man to use the concrete tile in that region. One cannot travel far in the country around Haseldorf and Wedel without seeing

*Fig. 21*

Wedel. The inscription on the back of this photograph reads as follows: 'Artificial stone factory of J. P. Jörgensen on the Englischen Berg in Wedel. The photograph was taken in c. 1900, and shows the owner with his wife. The building was completely destroyed by fire on the 21st June 1907'. In the foreground are stacks of bricks and tiles made on Jörgensen machines

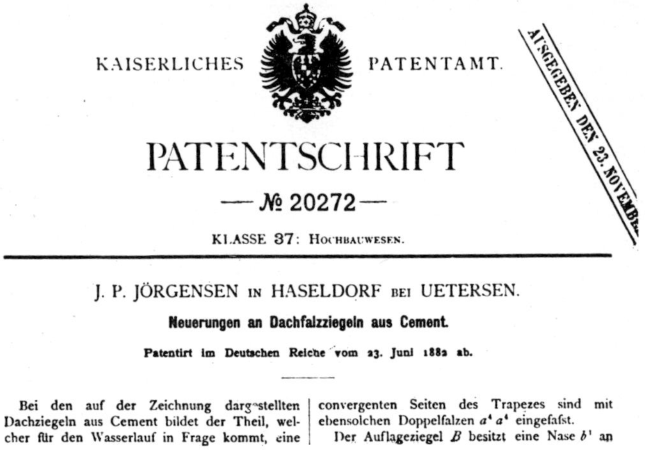

KAISERLICHES PATENTAMT.

AUSGEGEBEN DEN 23. NOVEMB

# PATENTSCHRIFT

— № 20272 —

KLASSE 37: HOCHBAUWESEN.

J. P. JÖRGENSEN IN HASELDORF BEI UETERSEN.

**Neuerungen an Dachfalzziegeln aus Cement.**

**Patentirt im Deutschen Reiche vom 23. Juni 1882 ab.**

Bei den auf der Zeichnung dargestellten Dachziegeln aus Cement bildet der Theil, welcher für den Wasserlauf in Frage kommt, eine convergenten Seiten des Trapezes sind mit ebensolchen Doppelfalzen $a^4$ $a^4$ eingefafst.

Der Auflageziegel *B* besitzt eine Nase $b^1$ an

*Fig. 22*

*Jörgensen's first patent for a concrete tile, No. 20272, dated 23rd June 1882*

examples of Jörgensen's concrete bricks and tiles. He may have brought his ideas from his native Denmark, for the Danes have been and still are adept in the making of concrete products.

We know little about his work between 1871 and 1882, but in the latter year he took out the first of his many patents for tiles, bricks, presses and other appliances connected with his industry: I have photostat copies of seven of them. The one of which some of the drawings are reproduced is his first, Patent No. 20272, issued by the German Royal Patent Office on the 23rd June, 1882. The photograph of an over-tile and an under-tile is of two samples collected from Herr Willi Pein's farm at Appen.

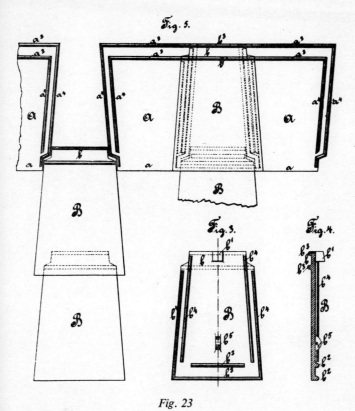

*Fig. 23*

*An illustration from the Patent No. 20272 (see fig. 22)*

Students of roofing will notice the close resemblance between these concrete tiles of Jörgensen's and our English 'Broomhall' pattern clay tile, made at Bridgwater. A number of English patents ante-date Jörgensen's; William Wilkinson

Fig. 24

Fig. 25

An over-tile and an under-tile made in 1887 under Jörgensen's Patent. The over-tile has D.R.P. 20272 UETERSEN on the back, Uetersen being the place of manufacture. These tiles came from the roof of an outhouse at the back of Willi Pein's farm (fig. 26)

took one out in 1805, and Thomas Taylor Coniam another in 1855. It is tempting to think that Jörgensen based his design on one of our English patterns, but we have no evidence of this.

Knowing of the German predilection for the sloping lower edge of a slate or tile, I was interested to find that in September 1883, in Patent No. 26201, Jörgensen registered improvements to the No. 20272 tile, and these included 'the angular arrangement of the edges of the water channel, so that the flow of the water is directed to the middle of the tile, with the result that the effect of the hollow shaped tile is obtained'.

The two Appen tiles came from a stack of a few hundred which farmer Willi Pein had recently stripped from a lean-to cattle shed at the back of the house. The farmer assured me that the tiles on the house and cattle shed were those put on when his father had the house built in 1887, and that so far as he knew there had been no trouble with the tiles on the roof of the house. Those on the cattle shed had been unsatisfactory during the last few years, perhaps because of the excessively slow pitch and the fact that the shed faces north.

Willi Pein was most helpful, but I must confess that his wife did not disguise her hilarity at meeting a mad Englishman whose insanity took the form of enthusiasm at the sight of a stack of 1887 concrete tiles.

Each over-tile is impressed with the inscription 'D.R.P. 20272, UETERSEN'.

Jörgensen built his first factory at Wedel in 1883, the one seen in the 1901 photograph. He sold it in 1902, and it was destroyed by either fire or explosion in 1907. Near the site of this old factory stands Jörgensen's show house, illustrated here. The bricks, roofing tiles, patterned floor tiles and other materials give a good idea of the excellence of Jörgensen's products. The red roofing tiles have faded and gathered

*Fig. 26*

*Appen: Willi Pein's farmhouse. The house on the left is roofed with
diamond-pattern concrete tiles*

*Fig. 27*

*Wedel: the Jörgensen Showhouse, built in 1903 partly for the display
of materials made by Jörgensen, and partly for the purpose of testing
tiles for weather resistance. The tiles, ridges and special verge tiles
were all fixed in 1903. The tiles on the slope seen in fig. 28 are
attractive in appearance but the side-lock is inadequate; this tile
was one of Jörgensen's less successful experiments*

*Fig. 28*

*Wedel: The Jörgensen Showhouse (see fig. 27)*

lichen, but the red bricks have retained much of their colour.

Jörgensen's second factory, built at Quickborn in 1895, is now run by Herr Paul Rademacher, the son of G. Rademacher, to whom Jörgensen sold the building in 1925. Rademacher had been established since 1895 in the same industry on the opposite side of the road, and this accounts for the wording seen in the photograph. The name 'J. P.

1899 Betonwaren 1949
Terrazzolegerei · Steinmetzbetrieb · Baustoffe
Paul Rademacher.

*Fig. 29*

*Quickborn: the second Jörgensen factory, now owned by Herr Paul Rademacher. He still makes a few interlocking concrete tiles like those on the roof, but only 'to order'*

## 1901.

# G. Rademacher

## Quickborn
(Holstein).

## Cementziegelei
## und Cementwaren-
## Fabrik.

*Figs. 30, 31, 32*

*Trade card issued by G. Rademacher in 1901*

40

Bei der Gründung einer Cement-Dachziegelfabrik
habe ich mich nach langer Beschäftigung mit der
Sache, sowie auf Grund von Gutachten von Autoritäten
in der Baubranche für

# Reisings

# Sattelfalzziegel

mit Doppelfalze (vielfach patentiert) entschieden.

# Das Dach der Zukunft.

Neu!     Ohne Mörtelverstrich.     Neu!

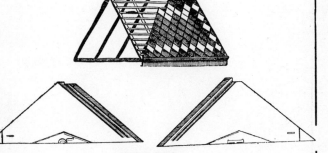

Seitenhalbe.

2

*Fig. 31*

41

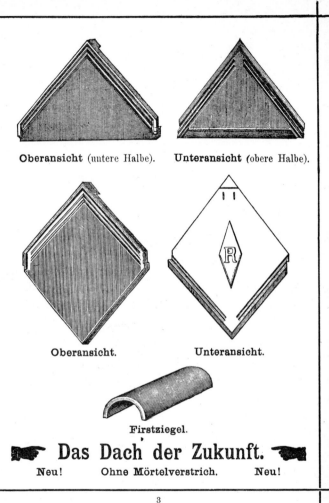

Oberansicht (untere Halbe).   Unteransicht (obere Halbe).

Oberansicht.                   Unteransicht.

Firstziegel.

☞ **Das Dach der Zukunft.** ☜

Neu!        Ohne Mörtelverstrich.        Neu!

3

*Fig. 32*

42

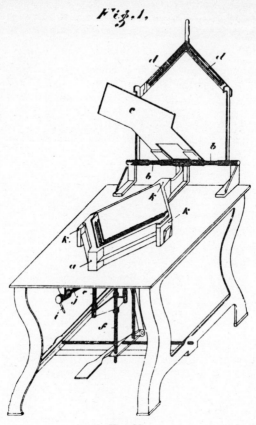

*Fig. 33*

The Reisings Sattelfalzziegel referred to in the
Rademacher Trade Card (figs. 30–2) was the
diamond-pattern tile made on this machine. The
patent is dated 3rd August 1898. The machine is very
similar to the Kroher machine. Reising's patent is
for an improved method of forming the interlock

43

Jörgensen', although long since painted out, is still faintly discernible.

I had two pleasant meetings with Herr Rademacher at his house near the factory; he supplemented what I had earlier learned from Herr Heinrich Jörgensen, and he kindly gave me what is probably the only existing copy of a card which his father issued in 1901. On it are set out the things which were then being made of concrete at Quickborn—floor tiles, paving slabs, cattle and pig troughs, drain pipes, roofing tiles, etc.—and Herr Rademacher announces on the card that after long consideration and after having consulted the authorities he has decided to make the diamond-pattern tile. He then gives nine reasons why he has decided to make this tile: weather resistance, no need for mortar, lightness on the roof, etc.

Our two visits to Quickborn, and our travels around the area in which Jörgensen worked, have impressed me with his importance in the story of the development of concrete products in North Germany, and I find myself wanting to learn more about the life and work of this highly talented Danish concrete engineer, who died in 1933 at the age of eighty-one.

In giving prominence to the work of Kroher and Jörgensen I may be unfair to other men of whom we in England know nothing. Kroher was, of course, the pioneer, and it seems unlikely that any further research will depose him from that position. Herr Althammer mentions Roding, Bad Reichenhall, Guben and Oberkassel as being early centres of production, and it may well be that at one or more of these places there was a maker whose work was equal in value to that of Jörgensen. At Oberkassel, for example, there is the famous Hüser pre-cast concrete works where we were given a sample of a tile made in 1895. The name of Hüser was familiar in the concrete world many years earlier than that, and the firm was in fact established in about 1850. The

*Fig. 34*

*Oberkassel: the Hüser Works. The tiles on the wing on the left—the original block, built of pumice blocks —were made in 1895. The main block was built in 1905, and the tiles were made at this works in that year*

*Fig. 35*

*Wiesbaden-Biebrich: the Dykerhoff Works. The date of manufacture of these tiles is unknown, but other buildings in the same works are roofed with similar tiles, made by Hüsers at Oberkassel. Dykerhoff report, with regard to the tiles seen in this photograph, that they are satisfactory, and that there have been almost no repairs*

works stand on a former bed of the Rhine, the sand is excavated on the site, and appeared to be excellent for any kind of concrete products, including roofing tiles. Hartwig Hüser took out a patent for a diamond-pattern concrete roofing tile in 1878, and in the same year he made his first tiles at Oberkassel, so he may have contributed as much to the development of the concrete industry as Jörgensen did. In the matter of the roofing tile, however, Jörgensen was certainly more adventurous and versatile; he experimented

*Fig. 36*

*Caterham, Surrey: diamond-pattern tiles made between 1900 and 1910, on a German machine*

with numerous types, succeeded with some, failed with others, and took out many patents. Hüser, on the other hand, made only diamond-pattern tiles from his Rhine sand and Portland cement (4–1) and we can vouch for their excellence.

47

*Fig. 37*

*Minehead, Somerset: the diamond-pattern tiles on this roof were made in 1898, and, so far as the builders know, no replacements have been necessary*

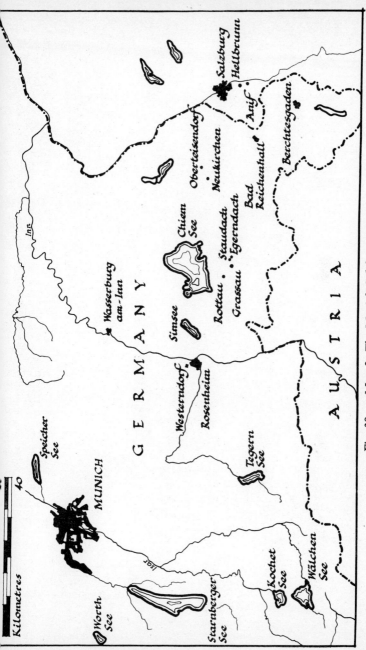

Fig. 38    Map 2: The Munich-Salzburg Region

*Fig. 39*

*Neukirchen, Bavaria: diamond-pattern tiles made in 1866*

The Hüser factory does not now make roofing tiles: a few were manufactured just after the last war, but the demand was not encouraging, and the machines were sold.

As with Jörgensen, I find myself wanting to learn more about the life and work of Hartwig Hüser.

*Fig. 40*

*Fragment of 1866 diamond-pattern tile from the roof seen in fig. 39, made from Staudach natural cement, with little or no added aggregate, showing extensive erosion by weather except on the right-hand side, where the tile was covered by the adjoining tile*

Another inventor of whom one would like to know more is Ludwig Nicol of Munich who, as a young man, was employed by the Reising Company. On the 21st October, 1899 Nicol took out Patent No. 115074, for a machine on which both roofing and floor tiles could be made. The roofing tiles were of a diamond pattern, similar to the Reising tile mentioned by Rademacher in his trade card. The Reising patent is No. 103522, dated the 3rd August, 1898. It is thought that Nicol, while in the employment of Christopher Reising and Sons, suggested the adaptation of the 1898 press so that floor tiles could be made on it, and that it was with the help and concurrence of the Reisings that his patent was taken out.

At the turn of the century the advocates of the diamond-pattern tile were confident that it would be widely accepted. Rademacher called it *Das Dach der Zukunft*—the Tile of the Future. That proved to be unjustified optimism because, in fact, neither in Germany nor in any other country did the tile attain any great popularity.

The tile came to England in about 1895 and two of our illustrations show it on roofs at Caterham and Minehead. The Caterham tiles are of some interest because they were originally fixed on a house in Croydon and were transferred in 1928 to the roof of the present Service Station. Minehead school was built in 1898. The tiles at both Caterham and Minehead were made on German machines introduced into England in about 1895.

When we set out on our first Marley journey I knew only a little about the early history of the concrete tile. In 1938 Mr. Owen Aisher had read a paper to the London members of the Institute of Quarrying; in it he had said that the tile had undoubtedly been invented in Germany, that Austria and Denmark had taken the idea from Germany, and that either the Germans or the Danes had brought the tile—the

*Fig. 41*

*Oberteisendorf, Bavaria: the pantiles were made in 1867; the walls are of pumice and sandstone*

diamond pattern—to England in the closing years of the nineteenth century. That paper was the starting-point of my enquiries.

## Munich-Salzburg Region

Map II shows the area in which Adolph Kroher chiefly operated, and in which many of his tiles are still to be seen. In the near vicinity of Staudach one can discover with fair certainty which tiles were made at his works, but farther afield it is not so easy. The reason is that many 'Kroher type' tiles were made on the presses that he sold. There can be no doubt, however, that his influence is to be seen in the roofs of many towns and villages of the Chiemsee region.

The house at Neukirchen is a case in point: its roof is one of our most interesting examples, and it merits more than passing notice. The two ladies who now live there told us that the house was built in 1866, and that the tiles on the front slope are what are left of the original diamond-pattern ones. The whole roof was stripped a few years ago, the good tiles from both slopes were refixed on the front, and the back slope was roofed with clay interlocking tiles.

This stripping and re-tiling had to be done, not because of water penetration through the tiles, but because so many had broken. The chimney sweep was no doubt responsible for some of the damage, but an analysis of one of the large fragments which we were able to retrieve has revealed the primary cause of the trouble. Little or no sand was added to the Staudach cement of which the tiles are made: the coarser particles of the cement, up to $\frac{1}{4}$ in., serve as the aggregate. It is a matter for surprise, therefore, not that so many of these 1866 tiles have failed, but that so many are still sound.

The cement came from Kroher's factory, but we may be sure that he did not make the tiles. He invariably used the

*Fig. 42*

*A pantile, made in 1867, taken from the roof at Oberteisendorf illustrated in fig. 41*

*Fig. 43*

*Staudach: roof of an outhouse at the Kroher farmhouse, showing how right-handed pantiles are reversed and used for the repair of a roof covered with left-handed pantiles. The original tiles were made in c. 1870*

*Fig. 44*

*Grassau, near Staudach: diamond-pattern and left-handed pantiles
made at the Kroher factory. Year of manufacture unknown, but the
tiles are more than fifty years old*

57

*Fig. 45*

*Staudach: a stack of old diamond-pattern tiles and ridges lying beside the outhouse seen in fig. 43*

Fig. 46

*Hellbrunn, near Salzburg: concrete interlocking tiles made in 1957. The Bavarian Alps in the background*

clean, sharp sand of the Tiroler Ache, sieving it twice to ensure correct grading, and the cement was sieved to exclude the largest particles. Whoever made those Neukirchen tiles was not a skilled maker, and one wonders if perhaps he was somebody who had taken up Kroher's 'Do it Yourself' scheme.

The farmhouse at Oberteisendorf has left-handed pantiles on the front slope. This roof has had the same treatment as the one at Neukirchen: the good concrete pantiles are on the front slope, and the back slope is roofed with clay inter-locking tiles. The pantiles were made in 1867, and the sample that we brought home appears to be as sound as when it was made, but many of them must obviously have been defective, or the roof would never have been stripped. This particular tile has been used twice on the roof, once as a right-hand and once as a left-hand tile. The method of using a pantile of the wrong hand is clearly shown in the photograph of the outhouse roof at Staudach.

The corner of Austria just south of Salzburg proved to be of enormous interest, because here we were able to see at first hand how concrete tile manufacture is carried on as a 'house industry'. There is, near Salzburg, a works which can supply tiles for a scheme like the one at Hellbrunn, but anybody needing small quantities can get them made, or make them himself, on one of the two hand-operated presses at Anif.

One of these presses is owned by the principal Anif farmer, Herr Rupert Mayr. His men make tiles when the weather is bad, but he also hires out the press to other people. The guest house which Herr Mayr built for his daughter last year is roofed with tiles made on his press. The Hellbrunn bungalow is also roofed with these tiles, but the owner, Herr Pfaffenhofer made them himself. Moreover, he won first prize in the 1957 Salzburg housing campaign, which was organised to encourage potential house owners

*Fig. 47*

*Anif, near Salzburg: the guest house built in 1957 by Herr Mayr. The tiles are natural grey in colour, and were made on Herr Mayr's press, bought in 1911*

*Fig. 48*

*Hellbrunn, near Salzburg: Herr Pfaffenhofer's bungalow, which won first prize in the 1957 Salzburg Housing Campaign. The interlocking concrete tiles are natural grey in colour and were made by hand on one of the Anif presses*

*Fig. 49*

*Hellbrunn: the bungalow in the foreground, built in 1957, is roofed with an unusual pattern of concrete tile, natural grey in colour. The bungalow in the background is the one seen in fig. 48. The mountain is The Watchman*

63

*Fig. 50*

*Tiles with 'snow noses', used as snow guards, made on one of the Anif presses*

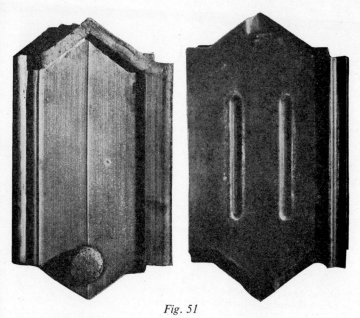

*Fig. 51*

*One of the Anif snow guard tiles, with its steel pallet*

to build their own houses: Salzburg had at that time an acute housing shortage.

We asked Herr Mayr why he started making concrete tiles, and he told us an odd story. In 1911, he said, a pedlar called at his farm and saw a heap of sand in the yard: the sand was from the River Salzach on which Anif and Salzburg stand. It happened that this pedlar had at one time been employed in a concrete products factory, and knew something about roofing tiles. He assured Herr Mayr that the Salzach sand was suitable for tile making. The farmer bought a press and has been making tiles ever since, and it

*Fig. 52*

*A diamond-pattern tile from Westerndorf, near Rosenheim, made in 1896. It has single ridges along its upper edges, and corresponding ridges on the underside. In the development of the diamond-pattern tile this type comes between the Kroher No. 5 (fig. 1) with no side locks, and the Hermannsburg tile (fig. 73) with its double ridge and channel*

66

is the 1911 press on which were made the tiles on the roofs of the guest house and Herr Pfaffenhofer's bungalow. That is how the concrete roofing tile industry started and is carried on in one Austrian village, and doubtless the story could be told, with only variations in detail, of many more such villages.

The second Anif press is, we gathered, owned by the community: we found it in one of the barns on Herr Johann Stellner's farm. On this tour my interpreter was a young student of philosophy at Frankfurt University, Franz Fuhrmann by name. Frau Stellner helped Franz and myself to clear the firewood under which the press was buried. It was a wet day and our shoes and trousers were spattered with mud when we came back from the barn. Our hostess insisted on cleaning our shoes, and pressed us to stay for coffee and cakes, which we had to refuse because we were in a hurry. This was only one of a number of occasions on which we were offered hospitality of this sort.

It was on this second Anif machine that the tiles with *schnee nasen* (snow noses) were made. These serve as cheap but quite effective snow guards, preventing large sheets of frozen snow from slipping over the eaves when the thaw comes. The 'noses' are made in quantity in small moulds, allowed to set hard, and pressed into the face of newly made tiles.


## North Germany and Denmark

This region, shown in Maps III and IV, would have been disappointing if we had gone there expecting to find concrete-tiled roofs as old as those we had seen in Bavaria, but we had been told before we set out that we should probably find nothing earlier than the eighteen-nineties. In the event, the oldest roofs that we identified were those at Appen, covered in 1887, with tiles made under Jörgensen's

*Fig. 53   Map 3: Schleswig-Holstein*

Fig. 54   Map 4: Hamburg-Hanover Region

*Fig. 55*

*Haseldorf, Schleswig-Holstein: Houses thatched with reeds in background; a stack of reeds in foreground*

first patent. There were, of course, old roofs in profusion, many of mellowed clay tiles, some of lovely reed thatch sixty, seventy and eighty years old, thatched barns with storks' nests built on old wagon wheels fixed on the crest of the roof.

Despite the lack of very old concrete-tiled roofs our tour was interesting and rewarding, because in North Germany and Denmark we were able to observe what may be called the intermediate stage in the development of the tile, and we were able to see modern concrete-tiled roofs, and works where concrete products are made.

In Bavaria we had seen the primitive diamond-pattern slab, its plainness relieved only by the large nib; and we had seen the simple pantile, a copy of the clay tile made for centuries in the Netherlands, and called 'The Belgian tile' in Bavaria. In Schleswig-Holstein we saw the later diamond-pattern tile with interlocks, like those made by the Rademachers under Reising's 1898 patent, and the yet more elaborate interlocking 'Broomhall' tiles designed by Jörgensen.

It was at Danischenhagen, near Eckernförde, that we saw our first roof of ornamental diamond-pattern tiles, made in the first decade of this century. The occupier, finding it impossible to buy replacement tiles after the war, had been making some for himself in wooden moulds. He gave me a sample, telling me he had used a rapid-hardening cement mixed with sand from the shores of the Baltic Sea. He had no technical knowledge, but he had made a concrete tile with a good half-century of potential life in it.

The bungalow at Bramminge in Denmark is roofed with precisely similar tiles. A local resident told us that the bungalow was built about fifty years ago, and that the tiles were the original ones.

I have included in this section a number of photographs that are fairly representative of the concrete-tiled roofs that we saw in North Germany and Denmark. The bungalow

*Fig. 56*

Mölln, Schleswig-Holstein: the reed-thatched windmill, built in 1826.
The present owners bought it in 1940, and last made flour in 1952.
It is now a gaststatte, and your tea is served with a silver tea service:
the plates, cups and saucers are Copeland-Spode china

*Fig. 57*

*Klausdorf, near Kiel: diamond-pattern tiles made in 1895*

73

*Fig. 58*

*Uetersen, near Hamburg: tiles made 1900–1905 under Jörgensen's Patent No. 20272. The tiles were fixed on this bungalow in 1924, having been brought from an older house in Uetersen*

74

*Fig. 59*

*Bramminge, Denmark: Ornamental diamond-pattern tiles
about fifty years old*

roof at Ellerhoop has a pleasing variation of the diamond-
pattern tile, and we saw a number of examples of almost
identical tiles of much the same period—the early years of
this century—between Hamburg and Lüneburg.

The German school near Burkal in Denmark is note-
worthy because it has a German master, and German
children who are taught in German. I am told that under
the terms of the treaty signed after the 1914-18 War, there
are German schools in Denmark and Danish schools in
Germany. The pantiles on this school were made in 1934 on
an 'Ideal' machine at Egernsund in Denmark. The farm-

*Fig. 60*

*Ellerhoop, Schleswig-Holstein: a variation of the ordinary diamond-pattern tile. Date unknown*

*Fig. 61*

*Near Burkal, Denmark: the German school, roofed with pantiles
made in 1934 on a Danish 'Ideal' machine*

house at Lindhöft has similar tiles, made in 1948 by an
Italian, Santus, at Eckernförde. These Lindhöft tiles were,
like most that we saw, uncoloured, but in the clean, smoke-
less air of Schleswig-Holstein they have kept their natural
grey colour very well.

*Fig. 62*

*A detail of diamond-pattern tiling, photographed at Wunstorf, near Hanover. The tiles were made at Wunstorf in 1899.*

Wittbek Bakery has a special interest for us, because it marked the end of one of a number of pleasant little odysseys. This one started in the office of Dr. Franz Randel at Hamburg, and took us successively to the concrete products works of Herr Neuenschwander at Boostedt, near Neumünster, to the School of Building at Eckernförde, to Dr. Saeftel, an Eckernförde architect and an enthusiastic student of old buildings, who was the Town Commandant of the Husum and Wittbek area during the war, and so to the Bakery. The mention of Dr. Saeftel's name to the Bäckermeister and Frau Schünemann gave us, so to speak, the freedom of the Bakery. We took what photographs we wanted, both inside and outside, and our visit ended with coffee and cakes.

The Danish pantiles which I have mentioned are all made on the 'Ideal' machine. We spent a morning at Kiel with Herr R. Rünkler, the agent in Germany for the Ringstedt Jernstoberi and Maskinfabrik, the makers of the machine. Here again we were hospitably entertained, and over our coffee and cakes Herr Rünkler told us of his work in Germany and of the slow growth of the concrete roofing tile industry in the country. He then took us to the Dubberstein concrete tile works at Kiel, where we saw a semi-automatic 'Ideal' machine at work.

During our tour in the Hanover–Brunswick–Lüneburg area we saw many good examples of the small diamond-pattern tile which is used only for wall cladding. We were fortunate in getting a complete tile from Haste School: the photograph was taken at the school of the neighbouring village of Helsinghausen.

I have included three photographs taken at the concrete products works of Herr J. F. Renner at Hermannsburg. The works particularly interested us because it was the only place where we saw a press for making diamond-pattern tiles. The machine is very similar to that illustrated in the

79

*Fig. 63*

*Lindhöft, near Eckernförde: a farm-building on left, roofed with pantiles made c. 1947 on a Danish 'Ideal' machine*

*Fig. 64*

*Wittbek, Schleswig-Holstein: the Bakery, roofed in 1910 with interlocking concrete tiles*

81

*Fig. 65*

*Wittbek: the interior of the Bakery roof. The rafters are 6 in. × 2½ in. fixed at 3 ft. 3 in. centres, and the battens are 2¼ in. × 1½ in. The horizontal and vertical torching extends over most of the roof*

article by Adolph Kroher the younger, to which reference has already been made. The output of a machine like this is anything up to 180 tiles per day: that is just about three minutes' output of a modern automatic machine.

82

*Fig. 66*

*Haste, near Hanover: a small diamond-pattern concrete tile used
for wall cladding. Date unknown. Similar tiles are seen in fig. 68*

*Fig. 67*

*Hasede, near Hildesheim: small diamond-pattern concrete tiles commonly used for wall cladding in this area. At the time of our visit a new window was being fixed in the first floor. On the upper edges of the tiles are the white interlocks, moulded on the tiles after they have already been coloured red*

*Fig. 68*

*Detail of small diamond-pattern tiling on the walls of the village school at Helsinghausen, near Hanover. The tiles were made in 1902*

## Conclusion

The concrete roofing tile was first made in Germany, it has been used continuously since the eighteen-forties, many of the early tiles are still perfectly sound after more than a century of exposure to the weather, yet the tile has never firmly established itself in the land of its origin. This is something of a paradox in a country like Germany, which in other ways has exploited concrete technique to the full.

During my conversations in Germany I have made a point of asking why the tile has not made the headway that might have been expected, and there was fairly general agreement on the reasons. The consensus of opinion may be summed up as follows:

Until comparatively recent times the manufacture of the concrete roofing tile has been carried on in small works, each of which has necessarily served a very restricted area. Adolph Kroher probably worked farther afield than most of his successors in the industry.

Many of these small works made very poor tiles. Works that were under the supervision of experts like Kroher, Jörgensen and Rademacher produced excellent tiles, much better than those made by some other men who used their machines and methods. Kroher's 1850 tiles, for example, are better than the 1866 tiles also made of Staudach natural cement. Similarly, a 1903 tile which was, as we know, made by J. P. Jörgensen is still sound, while the 1888 Uetersen tile, made under Jörgensen's 1882 patent, is of very poor quality. The difference is not accounted for by the difference in age: tests have shown that the 1888 tile could never have been a good one.

The inescapable truth is that in many places the concrete tile has been produced by inexperienced men. Where expert knowledge has been brought to bear the results have been good. The quality of the tiles that users of the Danish 'Ideal' machines have produced under the guidance of men like Herr Rünkler is excellent, and the same is no doubt true of many other producers.

The clay tile has always been a serious competitor of the concrete tile, and its competition has been all the more serious because the problem of colouring has never, until quite recently, been seriously considered in Germany.

The manufacturers of concrete products have been reluctant to invest money in tile manufacture, which might show a loss, when the money could be used for making other concrete goods that would almost certainly show a good profit.

The well-informed men with whom I spoke were all of the opinion that the only hope for the concrete tile lies in high production of first-quality tiles, in large factories.

In these pages I have given a brief verbal and pictorial account of the things learned so far in Germany about the development of the concrete tile. There are, as I have indicated, many gaps in our knowledge, and for my part I freely confess that I have only reached the stage at which all research workers arrive at some time or other, that of apprehending how much more is still to be learnt.

*Fig. 69*

*Beckedorf, near Hermannsburg: This barn was built in 1849 and was originally thatched. In 1901 the thatch was replaced by the present concrete tiles. The hips are covered with brown salt glazed stoneware channels. Across the whole width of the barn, at first floor level, is inscribed the lovely German prayer written by Hartmann Schent (1634–1681). It begins:*

> *Unsern ausgang segne Gott*
> *Unsern eingang gleicher massen*
> *Segne unser täglich Brot*
>> *(Our going out be blessed by God*
>> *Our coming in the same*
>> *Bless our daily bread)*

# EVIDENCE BEARING ON THE DURABILITY OF CONCRETE ROOF TILES DERIVED FROM A STUDY OF THEIR HISTORY AND DEVELOPMENT

By F. L. BRADY, M.Sc., A.R.I.C.

*Technical Director, The Marley Tile Company*

In the course of tracing the origin and history of the concrete roof tile, evidence has been obtained bearing on the properties and probable durability of such tiles and this is of immediate practical importance. There are four types of information which have been obtained by observation of existing roofs, by the study of the literature on the subject, and the examination of samples collected, namely:

(i) The condition of roofs of known age.

(ii) Records and analyses showing the materials used at various dates.

(iii) Tests of tiles of known age examined by the methods now used in official specifications.

(iv) Methods used for producing coloured tiles and their relative durability.

## 1. Durability and Mode of Weathering

The survey has afforded new evidence of the potential durability of concrete roof tiles. Samples have been collected which represent almost the first tiles ever made and which for over 100 years have withstood the ravages of time and have not yet reached the end of their useful life as roof coverings. In fact their present condition suggests they will last about as long again.

One of the most interesting points emerging from the

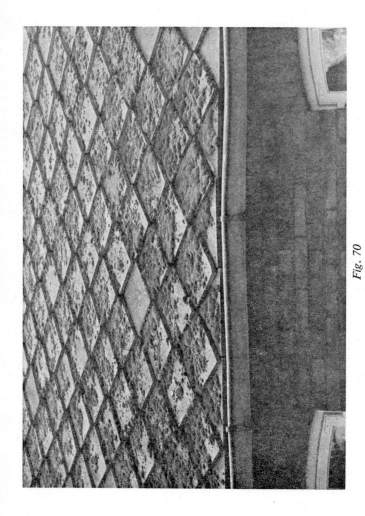

*Fig. 70*

*Wolthausen, near Celle: moss-covered diamond-pattern tiles made in 1902*

survey is that it has now become clear what is the essential factor influencing the life of the concrete tile.

The two types of roof tile are the fired clay tile and the concrete tile. These differ sharply as regards the factor which is important in determining their useful life.

## Clay Tile

In clay tiles the characteristic which generally determines the life of the unit is the structure of the fired body. The fired clay substance is virtually insoluble in water (even the acid rain of polluted atmosphere) but is liable to exhibit a laminar weakness which can lead to separation in planes parallel to the surface. This action, which is especially prone to occur with machine-made tiles—particularly those which are extruded—takes place when tiles which have absorbed some amount of water are subject to frost and can cause lamination in a few years. Some hand-made and, more frequently, machine-made tiles appear to be reasonably free from this defect which, however, is capable of bringing to a rather early end the life of tile in which the laminar structure is well developed, as is often the case. Since the action is connected with the joint operation of moisture and low temperatures it is much more prone to occur on roofs at low pitches than those at steep slopes. It appears to be connected with the tendency of the ultimate particles of which the clay is composed to set themselves in a direction at right angles to any applied pressure or parallel to a direction of extrusive flow. (There are occasional cases of breakdown due to efflorescence of under-burned tiles, chiefly affecting the unexposed head and nibs of the tile, but the chief factor affecting durability is that explained above.)

## Concrete Tile

In concrete tile, damage due to frost is not a cause of breakdown, a fact which is ascribed to the absence of a

91

*Fig. 71*

*Hermannsburg, near Celle: the press at the works of Herr J. F. Renner*

laminar structure and to the fact that, in general, the absorption of concrete tiles is low. Conclusions based on the evidence of examples of tiles which have withstood long periods of weathering are always open to the criticism that only those concrete tiles which were of good quality have survived. In this connection it may be remarked, however, that none of the samples examined shows even an incipient lamination or decay nor were any roofs found by Mr. Dobson which showed any evidence of frost action, even in districts near the Baltic, where severe frost is usual for three or four months of the year. The weathering of concrete tiles is demonstrated by the survey to consist of a process of solution by rainwater. This process is extremely slow and, therefore, observation of tiles over periods of exposure is essential to assess its effect. The survey has provided the examples of very old tiles necessary for this purpose. The examination of these tiles shows that well-made products are capable of lasting over 100 and possibly even for 200 years and demonstrate that provided a concrete tile is sufficiently non-absorptive it will be free from risk of frost damage or rapid solution and its durability is assured.

## 2. Materials

It has often been assumed that concrete tiles have always been made with Portland cement as a binder but the survey has revealed that this is not true. The first tiles were made with 'natural cement' at Staudach, using a material which is still produced though not, so far as is known, now used for roof tile manufacture.

In various places in the world there occur sedimentary rock deposits which contain a mixture of lime, silica and alumina, i.e. the essential ingredients of Portland cement, in such proportions as to yield a cementitious material on being burnt. Being a natural deposit the proportions of the

93

*Fig. 72*

*Half tiles made in the press seen in fig. 71, and interlocking tiles made on another press at the same works*

individual constituents in the rock vary from point to point and the deposits that have been worked generally do not show the same high proportion of lime as in the artificial Portland cement. Comparative typical analyses are as follows:

| *Natural Cement* | % | *Portland Cement* | % |
|---|---|---|---|
| Lime     ....     ....     .... | 57.7 | Lime     ....     ....     .... | 64.4 |
| Magnesium oxide     .... | 1.5 | Magnesium oxide     .... | 0.8 |
| Potassium oxide     .... | a trace | Potassium oxide ....     .... | 0.6 |
| Alumina ....     ....     .... | 5.2 | Alumina ....     ....     .... | 5.4 |
| Iron oxide....     ....     .... | 8.4 | Iron oxide     ....     .... | 3.3 |
| Manganese dioxide     .... | 1.8 | Sulphuric anhydride     .... | 2.3 |
| Silica     ....     ....     .... | 22.4 | Silica     ....     ....     .... | 21.2 |
| Carbonic acid     ....     .... | 2.1 | Water and Carbon dioxide | 1.4 |

Natural cements are burned at a lower temperature than Portland cement, the treatment resembling that accorded to lime, and this fact, in conjunction with the lower lime ratio, yields a material with a strength potentiality far below that of a modern Portland cement. Not only is the final strength attained proved to be low but its rate of attainment is also slow. There is often, however, an initial rapid setting and it was apparently the practice so to manage this in the moulding of a tile as to enable the article to be lifted from the pallet in a few hours. Prolonged curing in moist rooms protected from draughts and sun heat and occasional sprinkling with water were necessary to give the article the strength necessary for handling and fixing on a roof.

The sand-carrying capacity of natural cement is low and this was perhaps the reason for the use in certain tiles of a mixture in which, in place of ordinary sand, there was substituted coarsely ground natural cement, the whole tile thus consisting of an 'active' material. A sample of such a tile and its properties are noted in the Table (1866 Neukirchen). The permeability value shows that this tile was not, because of its use of natural cement, superior to later productions.

*Fig. 73*

*Diamond-pattern tiles made on the press seen in fig. 71*

Portland cement was invented, it is true, earlier than the first concrete tile. The date of the invention of that cement may be taken as that of Joseph Aspdin's patent—1824. The cement was some time coming into general use though it was employed as early as 1838 by Brunel in the construction of the Thames tunnel in preference to natural cement. It was introduced into Germany as early as 1856. The survey does not enable one to give a precise date for the first use of Portland cement in roof tiles. Analyses of tiles dated as late as 1888 and 1903 suggest, though they do not absolutely prove, the use of a cementing material more like a hydraulic lime. In Britain where the concrete tile was not introduced until shortly before 1900 Portland cement has always been used.

The study of the samples of various ages by no means indicates that the tiles were of exceptional quality. In fact, by modern standards, some of them would be regarded as distinctly inferior. The aggregates used varied from coarse pebbly sands to sands of rather uniform, fine grading which would not be regarded today as making for efficient, economical production or a good-quality tile. Sometimes the consistence of the mix was relatively wet, in other cases stiff and dry. The efficiency of mixing was not always good (see the Hermannsburg tile 1890, Table) and sometimes the consolidation of the mixture was inadequate (1896 Western-dorf tile). The conclusion is drawn that the general good behaviour of the tiles collected was not due to exceptional care in manufacture or technically high quality.

## 3. Present-day Specifications for Roof Tile as Related to the Assessment of Durability

In Section 2 the nature of the weathering process of concrete tiles has been explained and it is therefore apparent that, in specifications for the quality of the product, durability will be secured by tests which will ensure an adequate degree of resistance to water absorption and permeation. There exist tests for this property in both the British and German standard specifications.

The German test, Norm 1115, prescribes the following method: A ridge or dam is formed around the edge of the tile and the shallow tank so formed is filled with water until there is a minimum depth of 1 cm. over the whole surface. The tile is kept under observation for 24 hours and it is required that water shall not pass through the tile to the extent that drops can fall from the underside. Dampness not accompanied by dripping is not objected to.

In the British standard test (B.S. 476, 1956) a cap 4 in. square (10 cm. approximately) is fixed by waxing to the upper surface of the tile and water is admitted under a head of 20 cms. The pressure is maintained for 24 hours at the end of which period it is required that the rate of flow of water shall not exceed 0.02 cc. per minute. Considering the pressure imposed and the area under test the test may be regarded as a stringent one. It has the advantage over the German test that it gives a method of comparing different tiles quantitatively from the point of view of density of structure.

The German specification, like the British, takes the view that units which have an adequate resistance to absorption and permeation can be regarded as meeting the requirements for resistance to damage by frost, which is confirmed by studies of the properties of tiles of up to and over 100 years' exposure.

A selection of typical tiles of varying age obtained during the course of the survey have been tested by the British specification method and the values are given in a Table. There is a plethora of data in the possession of manufacturers of concrete tiles tested by the British method with which these results on old tiles can be compared. It will be appreciated that if the results on the old tiles had been in general superior to modern production then there would be at least some degree of doubt whether the modern specifications secured durability. If the old tiles were, on the other hand, all below modern specifications then there would be every assurance that modern tiles conforming with present specifications are of excellent quality though there would be some reason to suppose that the specification level had been placed unduly high. The actual position is that some of the tiles are below modern specification standard and some superior, as shown below:

| *Conforming with Modern Specification** | *Below Requirements of Modern Specification* |
|---|---|
| 1848 Staudach | 1866 Neukirchen |
| 1890 Hermannsburg, sample 1 | 1888 Uetersen |
| 1896 Westerndorf | 1890 Hermannsburg, sample 2 |
| 1910 Wittbek bakery | 1947 Rosenheim |

Some, therefore, of the old tiles are better than modern specifications required and some poorer. However, the majority of modern concrete roof tiles comply with the official specifications with a considerable margin, which leads to the conclusion that the modern concrete tile, of specification quality, has properties similar to the best of the tile collected during the survey.

The change in the tiles mentioned in the table due to exposure was in every case limited to surface solution and removal of material and neither by visual inspection nor in the application of the permeability test were there any indications of deep-seated softening, decay or lamination.

From the tests reported the general conclusion is drawn that modern specifications for roof tiles ensure the production of tiles which in general are of the level of quality as regards durability of the tiles collected from various parts of Germany since the inception of production and which,

*B.S. 476—limit 0.02 cc. per minute passing through area 4 in. square under a head of 20 cm. at 24 hours. All tiles except 1888 Uetersen and 1890 Hermannsburg tile pass Deutsche Norm.

by observation of many roofs in different parts of Germany, have been found to have adequate resistance to the elements.

## 4. Colour

The development of satisfactory methods of colouring concrete tiles is something which was accomplished in Britain during the second quarter of the twentieth century. Samples of tile coloured by methods which are now regarded as relatively primitive have been collected and examined. The method used was that of mixing pigment and cement to a slurry and applying it to the tile in this form or of working into the surface of the newly moulded tile a clay mixture of pigment and cement. As late as 1919 in surveying the field of roof tile manufacture Eugen Kroher,* the grandson of the inventor, referred to no method technically superior to this. In his list of tools used in making tile, reference is made to a 'colour sieve' which would be used for sprinkling the smooth tile with pigment or with a mixture of pigment and cement and he states that 'by dusting the tiles with colouring matter during manufacture any desired colour can be given to the tiles although the natural colour should, in the first instance, be preferred'.

The lack of durability of colour coats of this composition, their poor texture and liability to irregular efflorescence are now so well known that it is not surprising that a preference was expressed for a tile of natural colour. Even as late as 1954 Althammer in a review of the industry† stated 'the colouring is effected either by means of a coat of colour or by a complete colouring of the mass. When colouring the tiles by means of a coat of colour, the colour must be carefully and intimately mixed with the cement in colour sieves or colour mixers before applying it to the mouldings. After application it is smoothed over with a spatula. An

* Tonindustrie-Zeitung 1919, 43 Jahrgang, No. 55, page 443.
† Die Betondachsteine.

evenly spread coating of colour is obtained by several applications and smoothing over of the cement colour mixture. For colouring right through the mass the colouring additive should not exceed 10 per cent by weight of the cement content. Cement and colouring matter should also be previously mixed dry. Coloured grains of sand can also be used for colouring purposes.'

The modern method of colouring achieves a degree of durability which puts it in an entirely different field from the methods described. The modern process consists essentially in coating mineral grains with an enamel-like coat of pigmentary composition which is fired on to the surface of the grain at a temperature never less than 600° C. and, in the case of certain colours, reaching a temperature as high as 900° C. The mineral granules coated by the firing process are fixed to the tile by means of a pigmented colour coat. The nature of the process is such as to preclude the use of pigments of impermanent character and any colour which will withstand the firing treatment involved in the coating process will, of necessity, exhibit high durability. Thus the modern roof tile has a composition, as to the body of the tile, of a quality not inferior to that of the historic samples collected in the survey in conjunction with a colouring process of superior durability.

The surface of the modern tile has a textured surface which is more pleasing than the smooth surface of trowelled coloured coats and which weathers in a natural and pleasing manner.

## 5. Conclusions

The technical examination of samples of tiles of varying age in conjunction with the observations made during the survey as previously reported must be regarded as affording satisfactory evidence that tiles conforming with modern specifications as to quality and incorporating modern methods as to colour treatment are reliably durable for roofing. In fact, although concrete tiles have been in production for over a century there has not yet been sufficient lapse of time to show what the ultimate life of a well-made tile may be.

## WEATHERING EFFECTS AND PERMEABILITY OF CONCRETE TILES
## OF VARYING AGES*

| Name and Date of Manufacture | Description | Condition |
|---|---|---|
| 1848 (*circa*) Staudach | Diamond pattern, without interlock; natural cement and coarse siliceous aggregate (rounded) up to $\frac{3}{16}$ in. | Very little loss of substance. Now rough owing to solution of cement around surface aggregate. |
| 1866 Neukirchen | Diamond pattern; semi-dry mix; aggregate a natural cement containing coarse particles up to $\frac{1}{4}$ in. with a little siliceous aggregate. | Surface deeply pitted up to $\frac{1}{8}$ in. and generally rough, spongy appearance but limit of useful life by no means reached. |
| 1888 Uetersen | 'Jörgensen' pattern tile. Aggregate up to $\frac{1}{4}$ in. | Considerable loss of substance, the highest of any reported. |
| 1890 Hermannsburg | Diamond pattern tile. Some contain coarse cement lumps indicating inferior mixing; medium consistence. Voids not well filled in thin sections of tile. | Surface uniformly rough and pitted. Depth of pitting due to solution up to $\frac{1}{8}$ in. |
| 1896 Westerndorf | Diamond pattern; contains coarse pebbles up to $\frac{3}{8}$ in.; the coarsest aggregate of any sample in the group. | Aggregate everywhere exposed and pits formed due to solution up to $\frac{3}{16}$ in.; limit of useful life still far from reached. |
| 1910 Wittbek bakery | Interlocking tile; fairly wet mix and fine sand; mixing poor there being individual balls of undispersed sand up to $\frac{1}{2}$-in. diameter. | Strong growth of lichen but little loss of substance, the surface being only roughened. |
| 1947 Rosenheim | Beaver-tail interlocking; wet mix; some coarse pebbles up to $\frac{3}{8}$ in. | Practically no loss of surface. |

* Prepared 1958

| Name and Date of Manufacture | Permeability c.c. per minute (Specification Standard = 0.02) | Presence or Otherwise of Dampness on Underside of Tile |
|---|---|---|
| 1848 (circa) Staudach | 0.011 | Small faint damp area developed after 6 hours and remained until end of test. No dripping. |
| 1866 Neukirchen | 0.038 | No dampness or dripping. |
| 1888 Uetersen | 0.258 | Became immediately damp and dripped rapidly and water was passing rapidly at 24 hours. |
| 1890 Hermanns-burg | Sample 1: 0.0075 Sample 2: 0.031 | Sample 1: One small damp spot appeared after 25 minutes and remained throughout test; no dripping. Sample 2: Damp patch formed at 4 hours and spread over a fairly wide area of the tile and commenced to drip at $6\frac{1}{4}$ hours, subsequently partially drying up. |
| 1896 Westerndorf | 0.0033 | Damp spot developed in 2 minutes near an apparent fold in the tile; this became wet but no dripping developed and eventually the dampness partially dried; two other spots of dampness developed at 14 minutes and $3\frac{1}{2}$ hours, respectively, but these both dried considerably before the termination of the test. |
| 1910 Wittbek bakery | 0.00094 | Dry throughout test. |
| 1947 Rosenheim | 0.038 | Dry throughout test. |

# INDEX

The numerals in **heavy type** refer to the *Figure numbers*
of the illustrations.

108

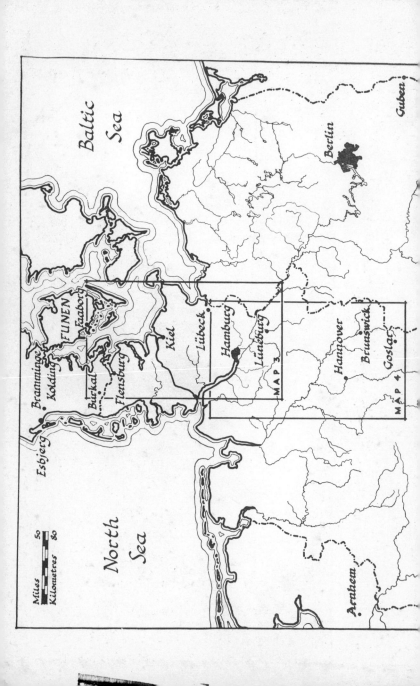

North
Sea

Baltic
Sea

Miles ⊢———┤ 50
Kilometres ⊢———┤ 80

Esbjerg

Bramminge
Kolding

FUNEN
Faaborg

Burkal
Flensburg

Kiel

Lübeck

Hamburg

Lüneburg

Hannover

Brunswick

Goslar

MAP 3

MAP 4

Berlin

Guben

Arnhem